Usborne Little Wipe-...
Word Book
Outdoors

Illustrated by Marta Cabrol

Designed by Yasmin Faulkner
Edited by Felicity Brooks

Trace over all the words in this book.

duck

pond

Out and about

sun

cloud

rain

rainbow

puddle

log

gate   bridge

rock   bush

lake   hill

On the farm

sheep

lamb

cow

calf

hen

chick

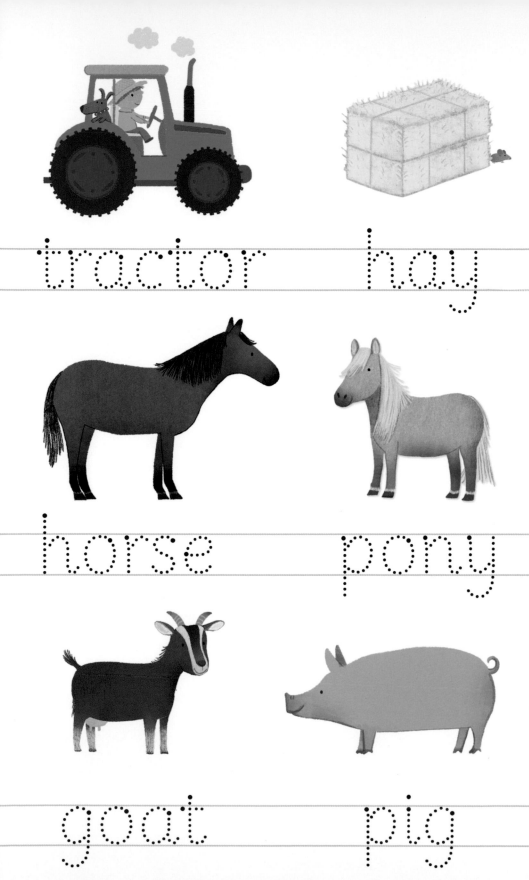

tractor   hay

horse   pony

goat   pig

Lots of bugs

wasp

bee

butterfly

ant

ladybird

moth

beetle spider

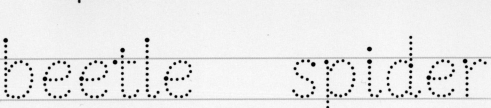

slug worm

caterpillar fly

Woodland animals

squirrel   rabbit

hedgehog fox

badger   mole

bear   cub   deer

shrew   wolf

bat   raccoon

By the river

toad

frog

dragonfly

newt

duck

lily pads

At the seaside

gull   seaweed

starfish   shells

mussel   crab

The wildlife park

penguin lemur

sloth meerkat

gorilla elephant

crocodile   tiger

lion   panda

zebra   monkey

All kinds of birds

swallow parrot

magpie pigeon

crow blackbird

pheasant owl

eagle hawk

swan flamingo

Pretty flowers

daisy dandelion

poppy bluebell

lavender pansy

sunflower rose

tulip buttercup

daffodil crocus

Leaves

oak

ash

maple

holly

beech

fern

Seasons

spring   summer

autumn   winter

Nature trail

twig   pinecone

acorn   nutshell

feather   catkins

pod

bulb

fossil

pebble

bark

lichen

Usborne Little Wipe-Clean
Word Book
Outdoors

This fun book is a perfect way for young children to improve their language and writing skills by tracing over 120 words to do with nature and the outdoors.

For advice about helping young children learn to read and write, and links to fun activities, go to www.usborne.com/quicklinks and enter the keywords "Early years activities".

£4.99
CAD$9.95

JFMA JJASOND/19
05428/1

Made with paper from a sustainable source.

www.usborne.com

CE

ISBN 978-1-4749-6814

9 781474 968140

First published in 2019 by Usborne Publishing Ltd., Usborne House, 83–85 Saffron Hill, London EC1N 8RT, England. Printed in China.

KS-732-620